Bastiens' Invitation to Music

For:

Age 4 and up

Time:

A Lifetime of Enjoyment

Hosts:

Jane Smisor Bastien

Lisa Bastien

Lori Bastien

kjos

Neil A. Kjos

Music Company,

Publisher

BOOK B

PIANO PARTY

CONTENTS

ISBN 0-8497-9553-2

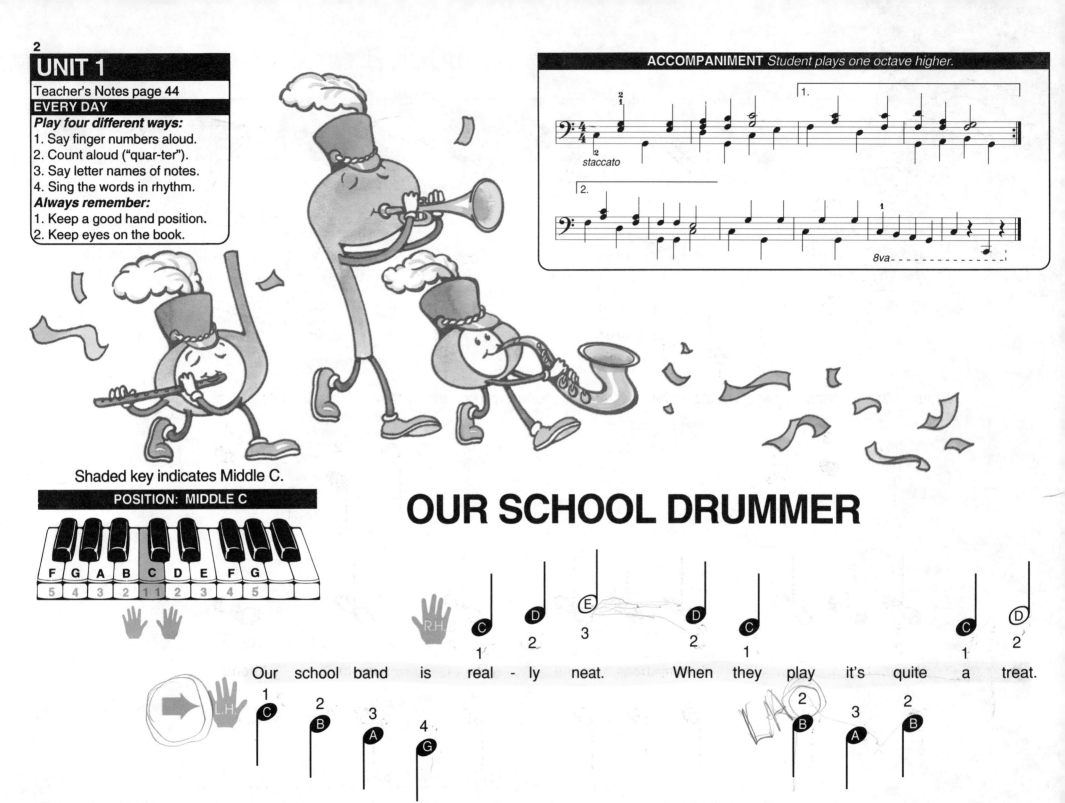

Play both hands one octave lower.

LEFT HAND PLAYING AND COUNTING

Using the correct Left Hand finger numbers, count aloud and play the rhythms.

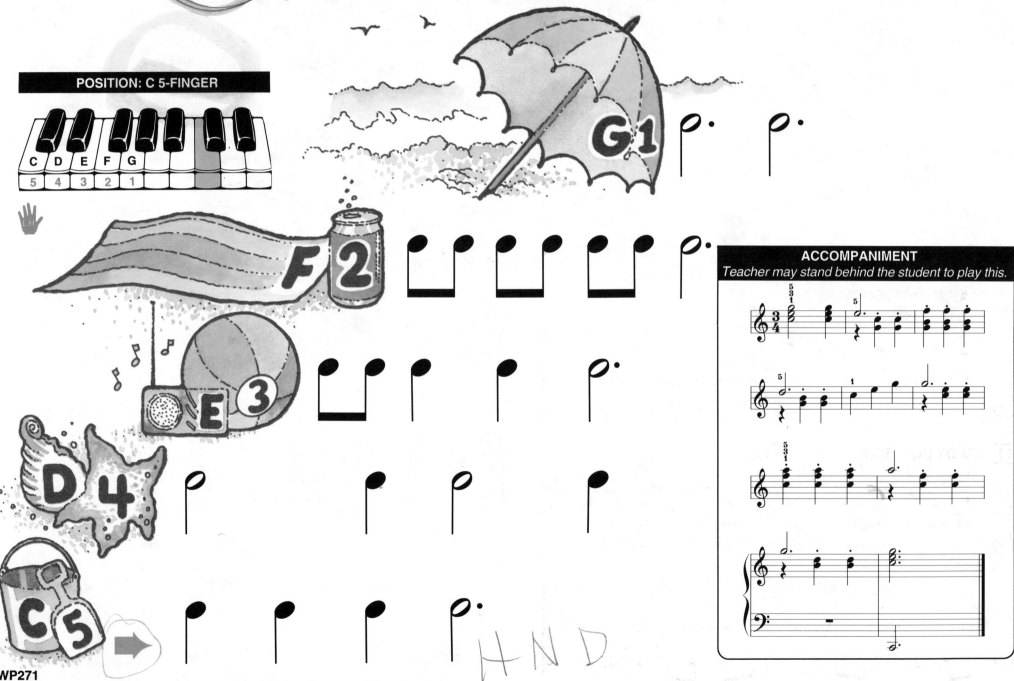

POSITION: C 5-FINGER

ACCOMPANIMENT
Teacher may stand behind the student to play this.

TAPPING AND CLAPPING RHYTHMS

A fun way to clap and count is shown by X's and dashes.

▬ = Tap both hands on
the closed fallboard.

X = Clap hands together.

1.

Tap and clap: ▬   ▬   X   X   X   ▬   ▬   X

Count aloud: Quar-ter   quar-ter   2   8ths   quar-ter   quar-ter   quar-ter   Half note

2.

3.

4.

UNIT 1
Teacher's Notes page 44
EVERYDAY
Play four different ways:
1. Say finger numbers aloud.
2. Count aloud ("quar-ter").
3. Say letter names of notes.
4. Sing the words in rhythm.
Always remember:
1. Keep a good hand position.
2. Keep eyes on the book.

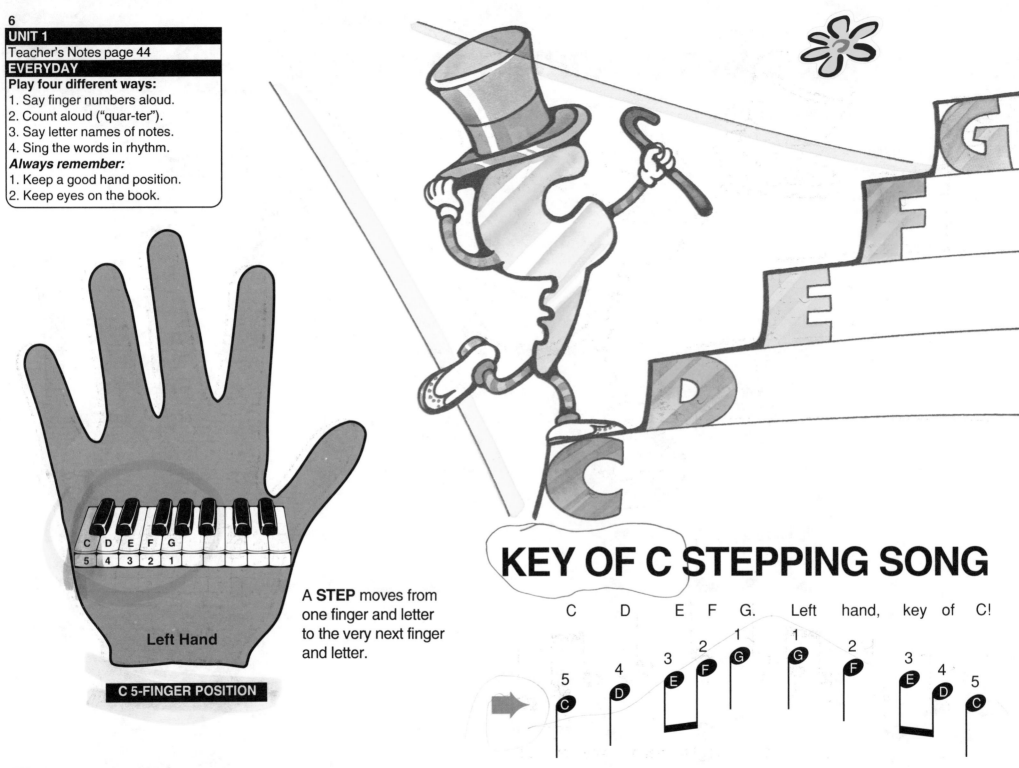

Left Hand

C 5-FINGER POSITION

A **STEP** moves from one finger and letter to the very next finger and letter.

KEY OF C STEPPING SONG

C   D   E   F   G.   Left   hand,   key   of   C!

Great!

8 Feb '05

C 5-FINGER POSITION

Right Hand

C D E F G
1 2 3 4 5

C D E F G Right hand, key of C!

WP271

UNIT 2

Teacher's Notes page 44

EVERY DAY

Play four different ways:

1. Say finger numbers aloud.
2. Count aloud ("quar-ter").
3. Say letter names of notes.
4. Sing the words in rhythm.

Always remember:

1. Keep a good hand position.
2. Keep eyes on the book.

ACCOMPANIMENT *Teacher may stand behind the student to play this.*

BACK PACKING

POSITION: C 5-FINGER

R.H.

Run-ning up the hill and walk - ing back.

Don't for - get to take your new back pack.

L.H.

PLAYING STEPS ALL OVER THE KEYBOARD

Play the steps below in the rhythms given on the keyboard. Count aloud, please!

1.

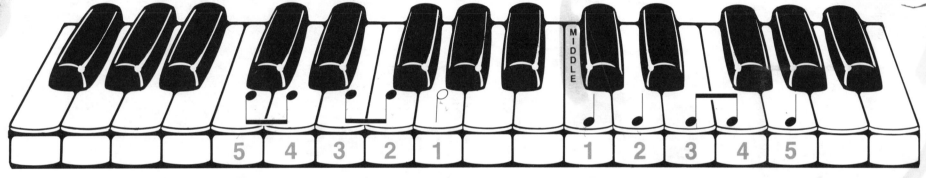

2.

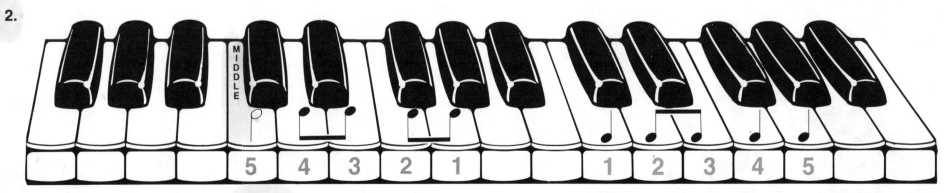

UNIT 2
Teacher's Notes page 44
EVERY DAY

Play four different ways:
1. Say finger numbers aloud.
2. Count aloud ("quar-ter").
3. Say letter names of notes.
4. Sing the words in rhythm.

Always remember:
1. Keep a good hand position.
2. Keep eyes on the book.

ACCOMPANIMENT *Student plays one octave higher.*

GOIN' FISHIN'

POSITION: C 5-FINGER

I'm goin' fish - in'   Sat - ur - day!   Please come with me,   spend the day!

PLAYING SKIPS ALL OVER THE KEYBOARD

A **SKIP** skips a **finger** and a **letter**.

Play the skips below in the rhythms given on the keyboards. Count aloud, please!

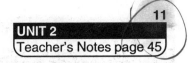

1.

2.

WP271

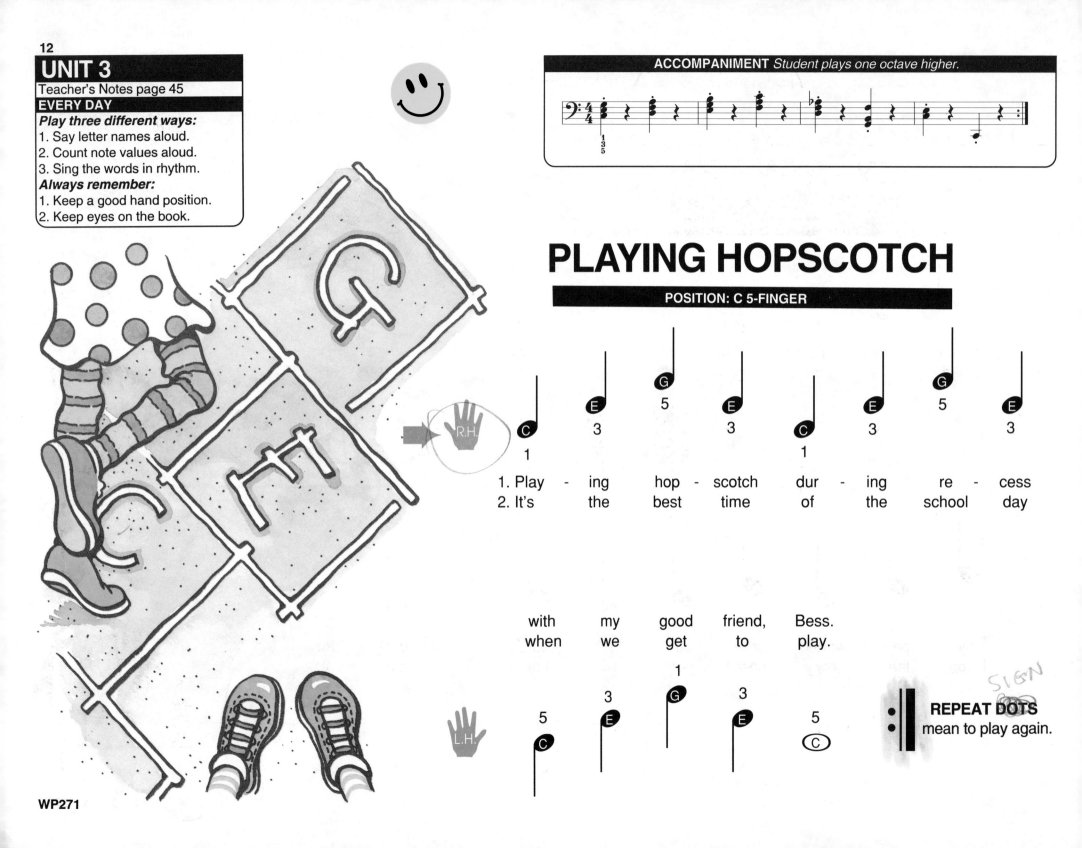

ACCOMPANIMENT *Student plays one octave higher.*

UNIT 3
Teacher's Notes page 45
EVERY DAY
Play three different ways:
1. Say letter names aloud.
2. Count note values aloud.
3. Sing the words in rhythm.
Always remember:
1. Keep a good hand position.
2. Keep eyes on the book.

READY FOR BED

POSITION: C 5-FINGER

Each night when it's time for bed, Moth - er says to me:

"Brush your teeth and wash your face. Then we'll read 'In Out - er Space.'"

WP271

UNIT 3
See Teacher's Notes page 45

EVERY DAY

Play three different ways:
1. Say letter names aloud.
2. Count note values aloud.
3. Sing the words in rhythm.

Always remember:
1. Keep a good hand position.
2. Keep eyes on the book.

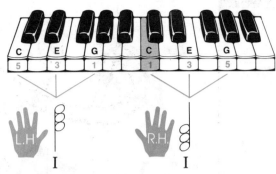

The **I CHORD** has **two skips.**

PLAYING THE I CHORD

POSITION: C 5-FINGER

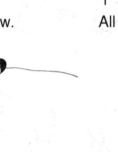

R.H. All three notes, I'll show you how.

Ev - 'ry oth - er fin - ger now.

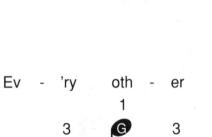

Play your I (one) chords. Take a bow!

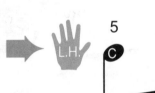

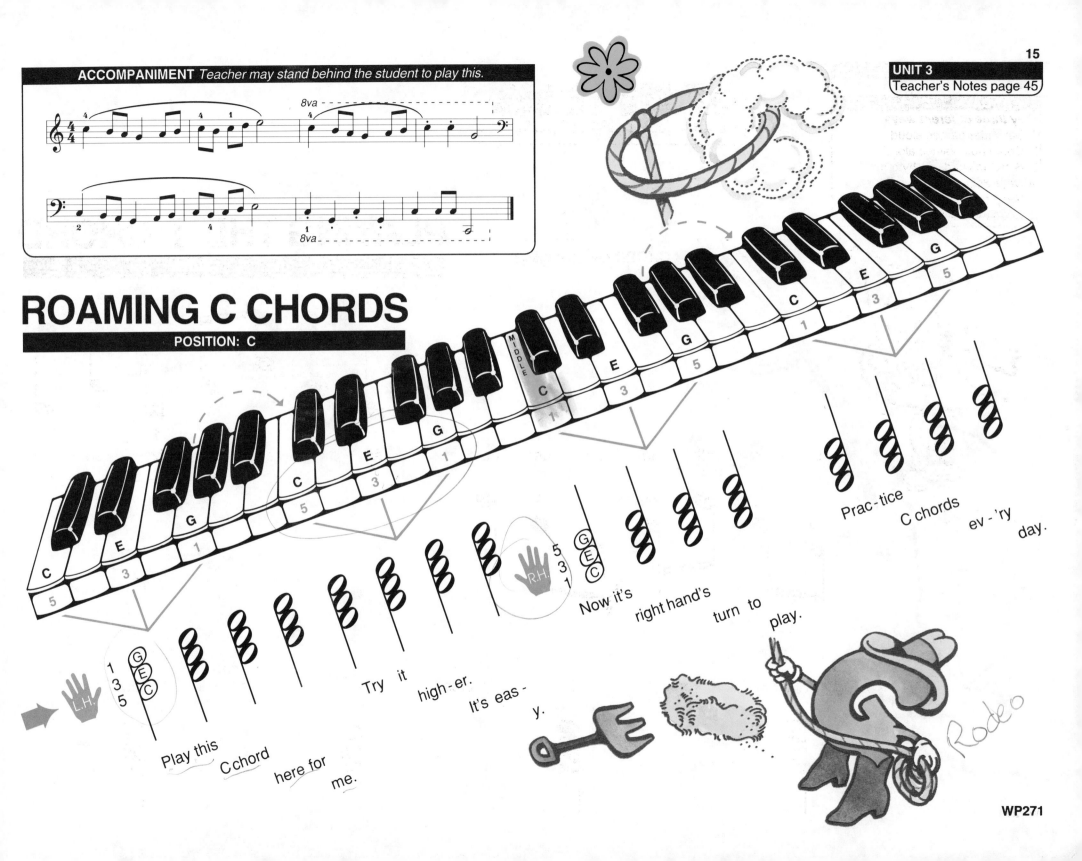

UNIT 4
Teacher's Notes page 46

POSITION: G 5-FINGER

KEY OF G SONG

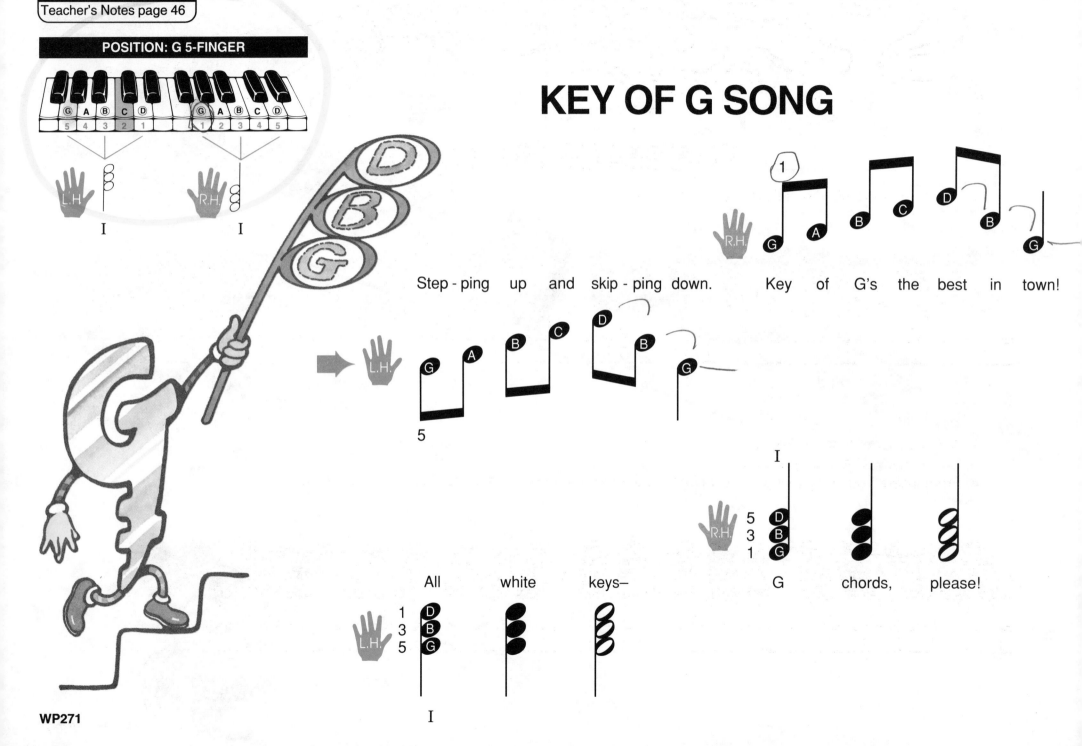

Step - ping up and skip - ping down.   Key of G's the best in town!

All   white   keys–   G   chords,   please!

ACCOMPANIMENT

8va

UNIT 4
Teacher's Notes page 46

EVERY DAY

Play three different ways:
1. Say letter names aloud.
2. Count note values aloud.
3. Sing the words in rhythm.

Always remember:
1. Keep a good hand position.
2. Keep eyes on the book.

THE BUSY AIRPORT

POSITION: G 5-FINGER

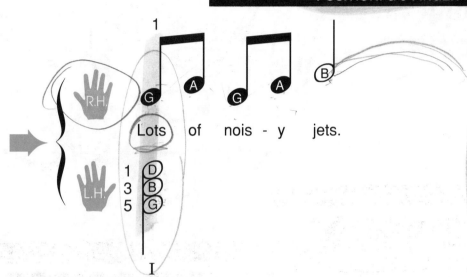

R.H.

G — A — G — A — B   G — A — G — A — B

Lots   of   nois - y   jets.   Peo - ple   rush - ing   by.

L.H. 1 D / 3 B / 5 G

I   I

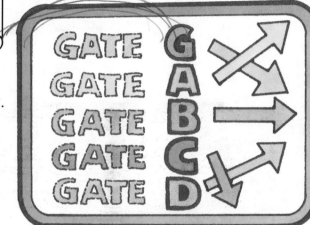

GATE GATE GATE GATE GATE   G A B C D

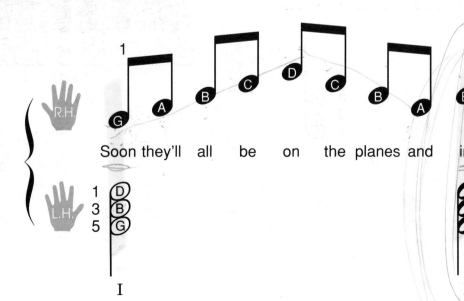

R.H.

G — A — B — C — D — C — B — A — B — A   G

Soon they'll   all   be   on   the planes and   in   the   sky.

L.H. 1 D / 3 B / 5 G

I   I

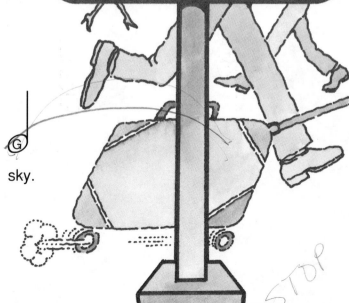

UNIT 4
Teacher's Notes page 46

EVERY DAY

Play three different ways:
1. Say letter names aloud.
2. Count note values aloud.
3. Sing the words in rhythm.

Always remember:
1. Keep a good hand position.
2. Keep eyes on the book.

ACCOMPANIMENT

SATURDAY MORNINGS

POSITION: G 5-FINGER

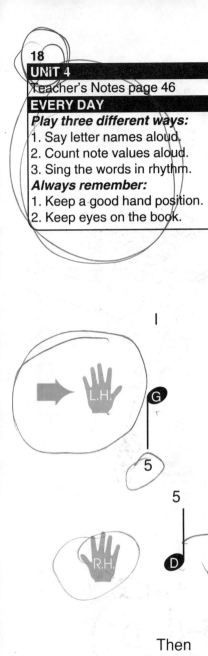

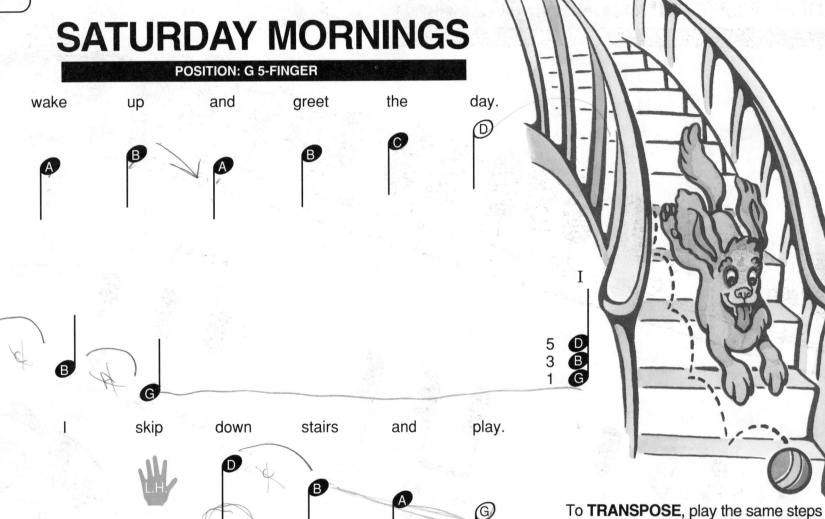

I wake up and greet the day.

Then I skip down stairs and play.

To **TRANSPOSE**, play the same steps and skips in another position.
Transpose "Saturday Mornings" to the C five-finger position.

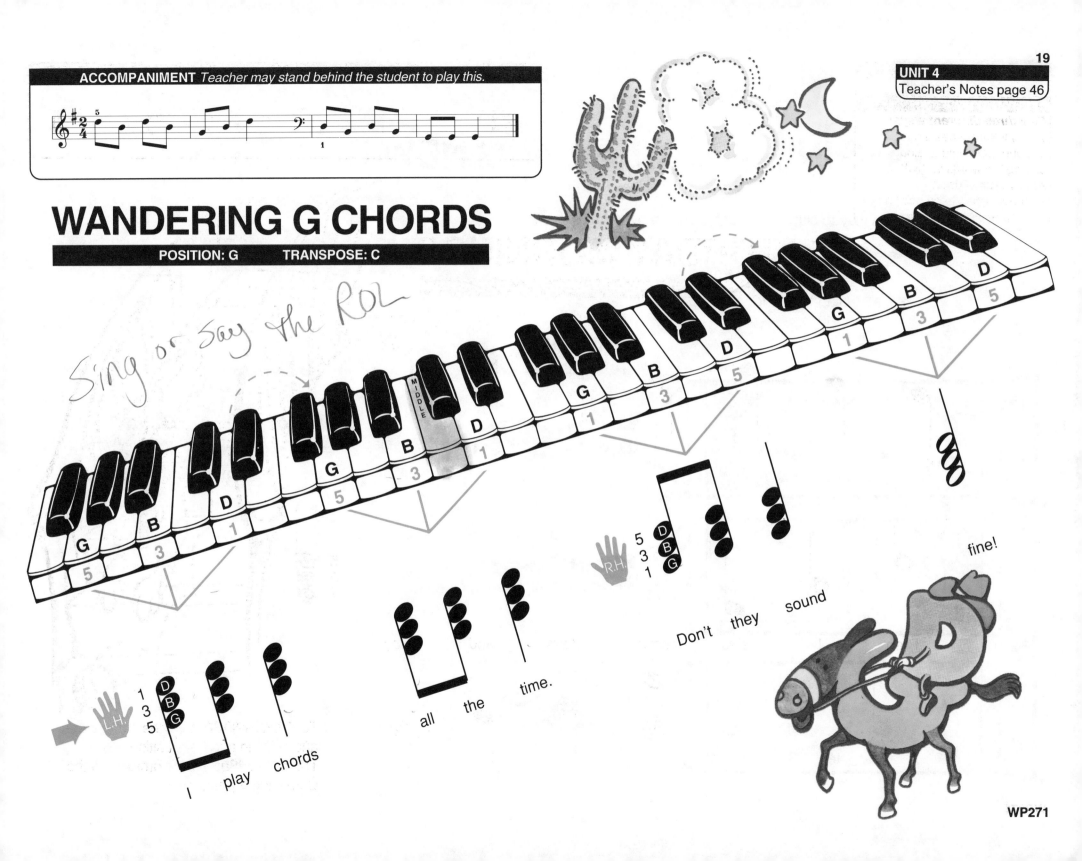

TAPPING AND CLAPPING NEW RHYTHMS

A fun way to clap and count is shown by X's and dashes.

▬ = Tap both hands on
the closed fallboard.

X = Clap hands together.

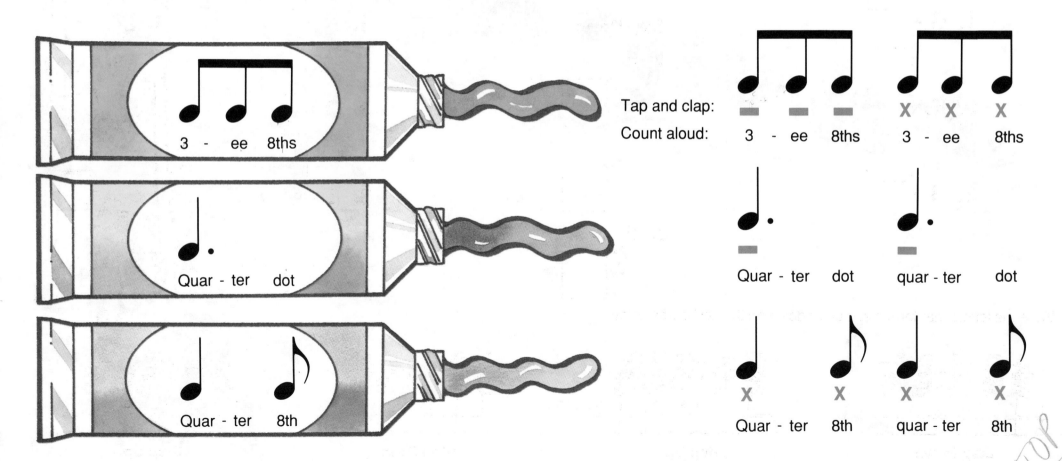

Tap and clap:
▬ ▬ ▬   X X X

Count aloud: 3 - ee 8ths   3 - ee 8ths

Quar - ter dot   quar - ter dot

Quar - ter 8th   quar - ter 8th

NEW RHYTHMS FOR THE RIGHT HAND

Using the correct Right Hand finger numbers, count aloud and play the following rhythms.

POSITION: G

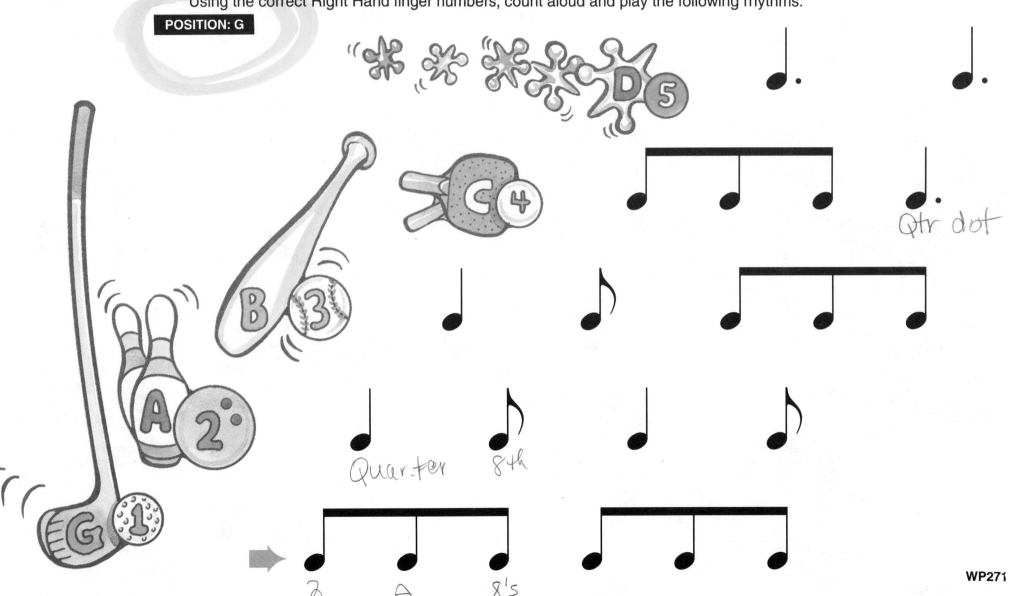

Qtr dot

Quarter   8th

3   e   8's

WP271

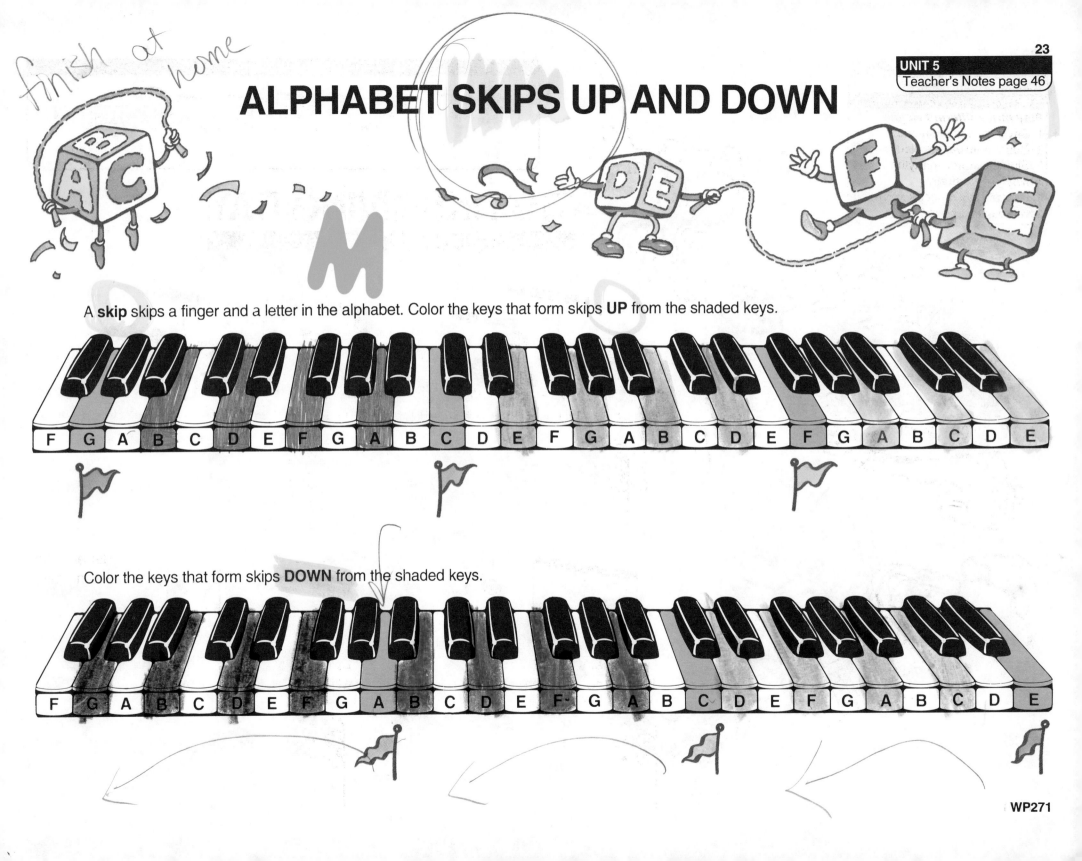

ALPHABET SKIPS UP AND DOWN

A **skip** skips a finger and a letter in the alphabet. Color the keys that form skips **UP** from the shaded keys.

Color the keys that form skips **DOWN** from the shaded keys.

UNIT 5
Teacher's Notes page 46

EVERY DAY

Play three different ways:
1. Say letter names aloud.
2. Count note values aloud.
3. Sing the words in rhythm.

Always remember:
1. Keep a good hand position.
2. Keep eyes on the book.

ACCOMPANIMENT

BIKE RACE

POSITION: G 5-FINGER
TRANSPOSE: C

See all the bi - cy - cles read - y to race.

Who do you think will win first place?

HIDING AND SEEKING SKIPS

UNIT 5
Teacher's Notes page 46
EVERY DAY
1. Find position using either hand.
2. Keep your eyes on the book.
3. Begin with the given letter and play the following skips.
   Answer the questions aloud as you play.

KEY OF C:

Up a skip?
Up a skip?
Down a skip?

Up a skip?
Down a skip?
Down a skip?

Down a skip?
Down a skip?
Up a skip?

KEY OF G:

Up a skip?
Up a skip?
Down a skip?

Down a skip?
Down a skip?
Up a skip?

Down a skip?
Up a skip?
Up a skip?

WP271

UNIT 6

Teachers Notes page 47

EVERY DAY

Play three different ways:
1. Say letter names aloud.
2. Count note values aloud.
3. Sing the words in rhythm.

Always remember:
1. Keep a good hand position.
2. Keep eyes on the book.

POSITION: F 5-FINGER

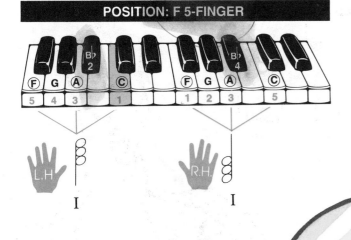

KEY OF F SONG

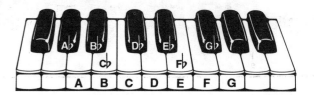

To make a note **FLAT**, play **DOWN** (left) to the nearest key. It may be either black or white. This sign, ♭, is a flat sign.

F   G   A   B♭   C.

F   has   one   black   key.

I   chord   though—

All   white keys   you   know.

ACCOMPANIMENT

staccato

8va

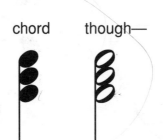

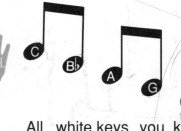

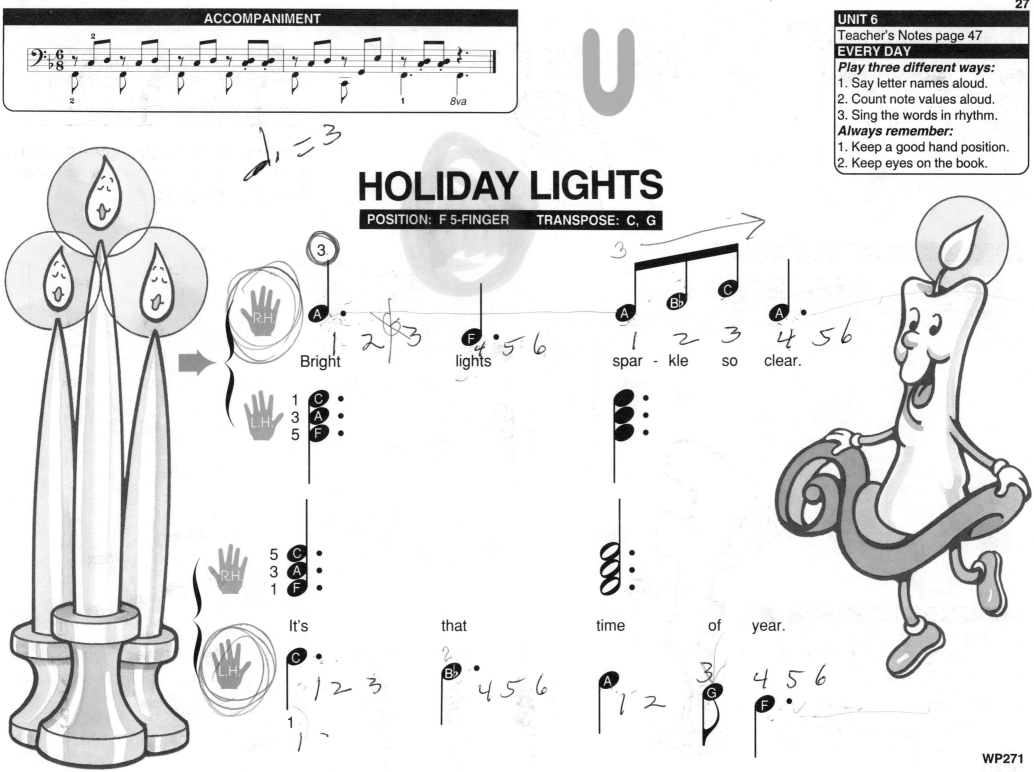

ALPHABET STEPS UP AND DOWN

A step moves from one key to the nearest key and from one letter to the nearest letter up or down.

Write the letters that form alphabet steps up or down.

Step Up

1. G ↗

2. F ↗

3. B ↗

Step Down

1. E ↘

2. C ↘

3. F ↘

Step Up

1. A ↗

2. D ↗

3. E ↗

Write the letters that form steps up or down on the keyboards below.

 E
Step Down

 F
Step Up

 A
Step Down

 G
Step Up

WP271

UNIT 6
EVERY DAY
1. Find your position using either hand.
2. Keep your eyes on the book.
3. Begin with the given letter and play the following skips and steps. Answer the questions aloud as you play.

HIDING AND SEEKING:
SKIPS AND STEPS

KEY OF F:

Up a step?
Up a step?
Up a skip?

Up a step?
Up a step?
Down a skip?

Down a step?
Down a skip?
Up a step?

KEY OF G:

Up a step?
Down a skip?
Up a step?

Down a step?
Up a skip?
Down a step?

Down a skip?
Down a skip?
Up a step?

ACCOMPANIMENT

8va

UNIT 6
Teacher's Notes page 47
EVERY DAY
Play three different ways.
1. Say letter names aloud.
2. Count note values aloud.
3. Sing the words in rhythm.
Always remember:
1. Keep a good hand position.
2. Keep eyes on the book.

WATCH THE CALENDAR

POSITION: F 5-FINGER   TRANSPOSE: C, G

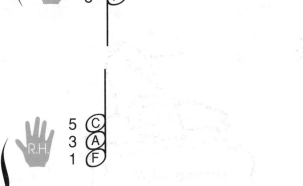

R.H. — 1 **F** **A** **C** **Bb** **A** **F** **A** **A** **C**

Watch   the   cal - en - dar   ev -   'ry   day.

L.H. — 1 3 5 **C** **A** **F**

R.H. — 5 3 1 **C** **A** **F**

Hap - py   New Year   is   on   the   way.

L.H. — 1 **C** **Bb** **A** **Bb** **C** **A** **G** **F**

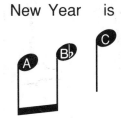

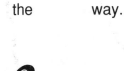

WP271

GROUP 1 KEYS

C G F

The **Group 1** keys are **C, G,** and **F** because they have **ALL WHITE KEYS** in their I chords. The **UNUSUAL** key in Group 1 is **F** because in the five-finger position there is a **BLACK KEY** under the **Left Hand 2**nd finger and the **Right Hand 4**th finger.

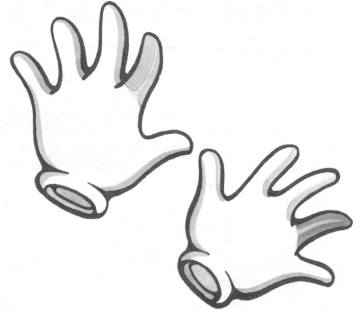

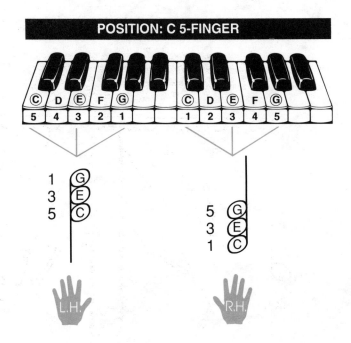

POSITION: C 5-FINGER

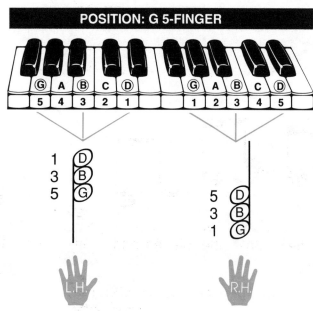

POSITION: G 5-FINGER

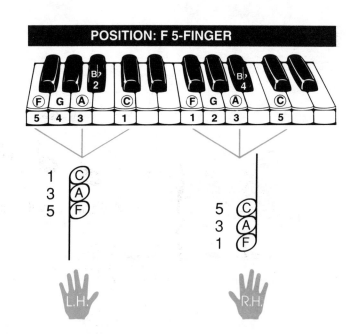

POSITION: F 5-FINGER

THE MAGICAL HARP

1. Begin on low **C** with Left Hand 5 and play skips up.

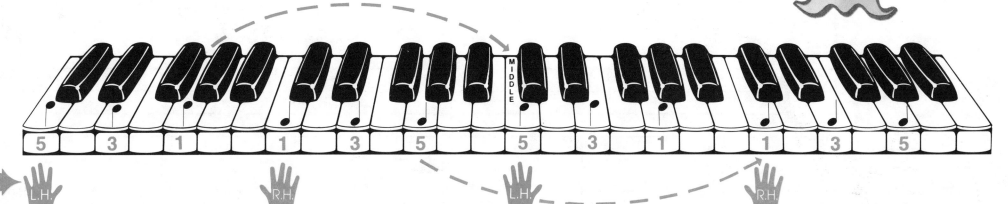

2. Begin on low **F** and play skips up.
3. Begin on low **G** and play skips up.
4. From where you end playing skips up from G, then play 4 on **C** and skip **down** in the C position.

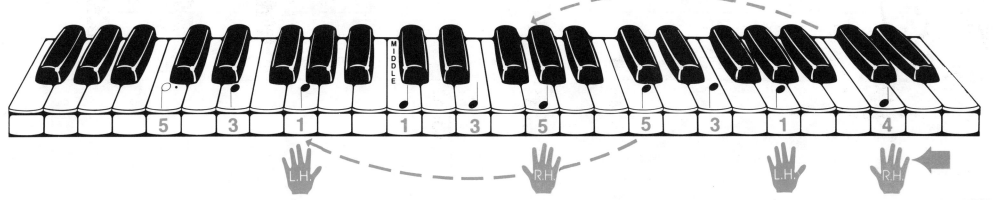

WP271

THE GRAND STAFF

Music is written on the **GRAND STAFF.**

TREBLE STAFF

BASS STAFF

The **upper** part of the Grand Staff is called the **TREBLE STAFF**. It has a treble (**G clef**) sign and five lines. Notes may be written in the four spaces between the lines as well as below and above the staff.

The **lower** part of the Grand Staff is called the **BASS STAFF**. It has a bass (**F clef**) sign and five lines. Notes may be written in the four spaces between the lines as well as below and above the staff.

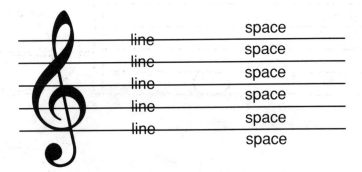

space
line
line
space
line
space
line
space
line
space
space

space
line
line
space
line
space
line
space
line
space
space

■ Trace the lines of the Grand Staff above with a green crayon.

■ Color the spaces of the Grand Staff above with an orange crayon.

LINE AND SPACE NOTES

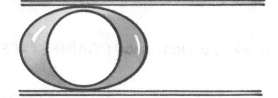

This is a **LINE** note.
The line goes **through** the note.

This is a **SPACE** note.
The note is **in** the space.

■Color the **line** notes red. ■Color the **space** notes blue.

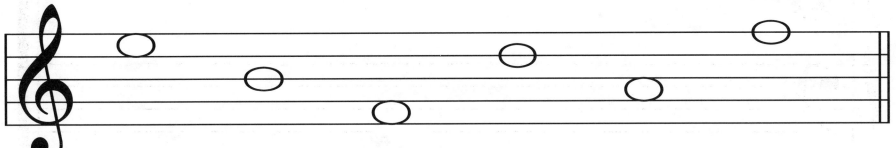

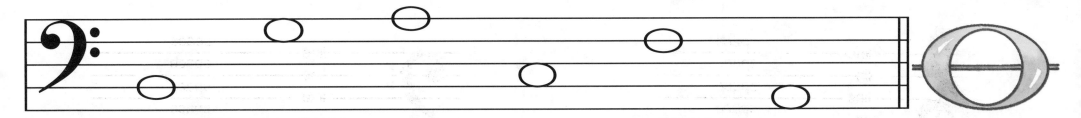

Draw some line and space notes.

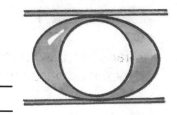

FUN WITH V7

POSITION: G 5-FINGER   TRANSPOSE: C, F

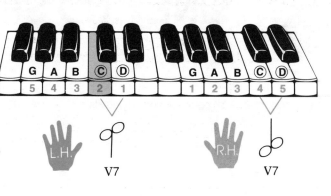

STACCATO DOTS over or under notes mean to play in a short detached manner (staccato).

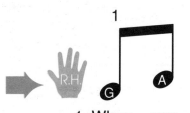

1. When you play the top two keys at one time,
2. It's a nice five sev - en chord you will see.

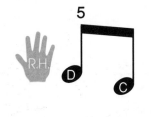

Then you have a new chord. It sounds fine.
It will work in all keys eas - i - ly.

ACCOMPANIMENT *Student plays one octave higher.*

WP271

UNIT 8
Teacher's Notes page 49
EVERY DAY

ACCOMPANIMENT

8va

MY NEW PEN

POSITION: C 5-FINGER
TRANSPOSE: F, G

Play three different ways:
1. Say letter names aloud.
2. Count note values aloud.
3. Sing the words in rhythm.
Always remember:
1. Keep a good hand position.
2. Keep eyes on the book.

R.H.
3
E   D   E   C .

F   E   F   D .

1. My   pen   writes   red.
2. What   a   great   pen.

My   pen   writes   blue.
Eas - y   to   hold.

L.H.
1 G
3 E
5 C
I

F G
1
2
V7

R.H.
5
G   F   E   F   E   D   E   D   C .

My   pen   writes   three   oth - er   col - ors   too!
Hope   that   my   new   pen   will   not   get   old.

L.H.
1 G
3 E
5 C
I

WP271

SKIPPING ON THE STAFF

A **SKIP** moves from one **line to the very next line** up or down,   OR   a **SKIP** moves from one **space to the very next space** up or down.

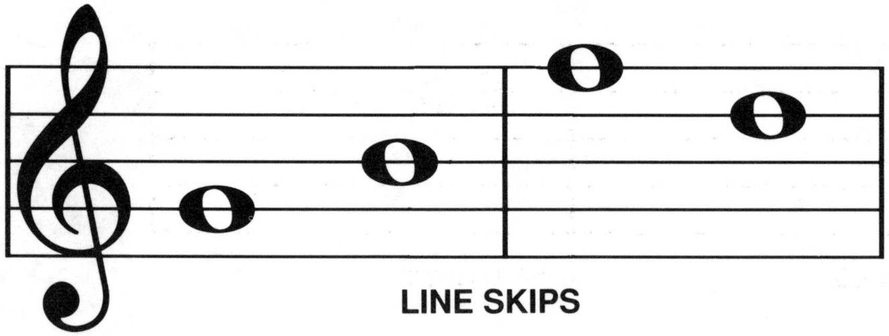

LINE SKIPS

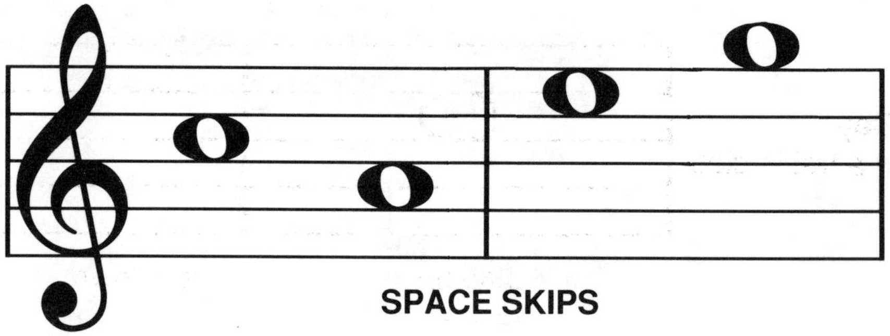

SPACE SKIPS

■ Color the **line** notes red. ■ Color the **space** notes blue.

Draw arrows to show whether skips are **up** or **down** on the staff.

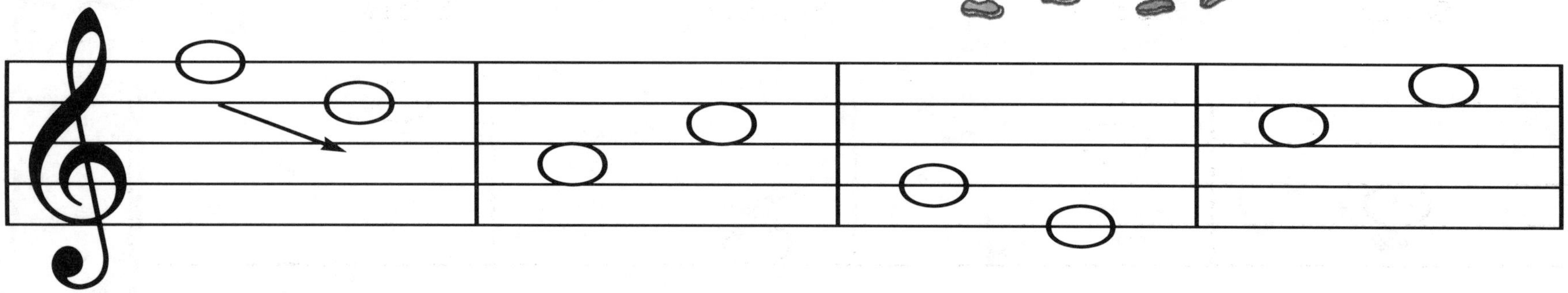

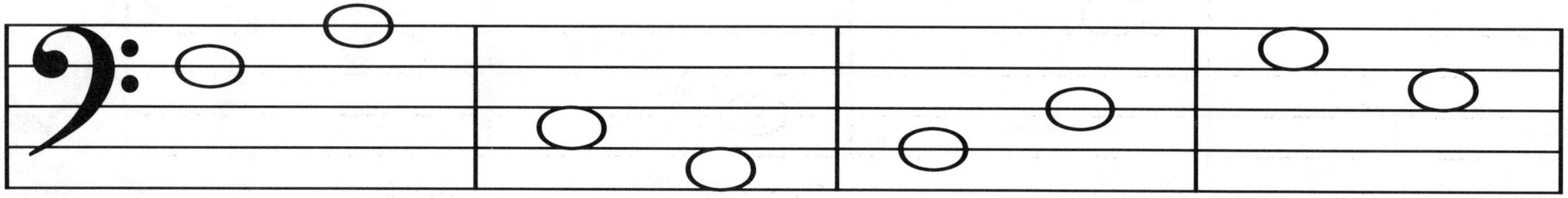

WP271

DRAWING SKIPS

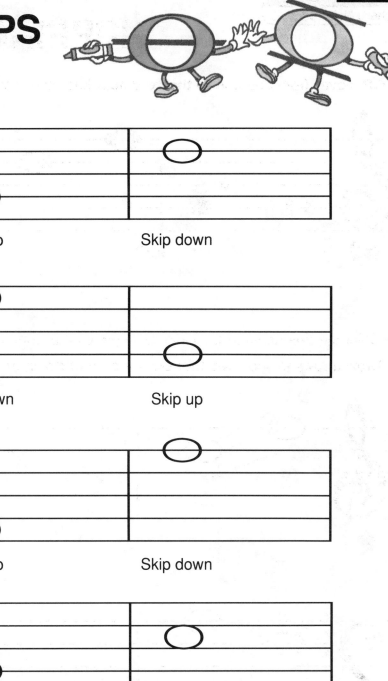

Draw the notes that form skips up or down from the given notes.
■ Color the **line** notes red.   ■ Color the **space** notes blue.

1st Day
Draw a treble clef.

Skip up   Skip down   Skip up   Skip down

2nd Day
Draw a bass clef.

Skip up   Skip down   Skip down   Skip up

3rd Day
Draw a treble clef.

Skip down   Skip up   Skip up   Skip down

4th Day
Draw a bass clef.

Skip up   Skip down   Skip down   Skip down

WHEN THE SAINTS COME MARCHING IN

POSITION: C 5-FINGER

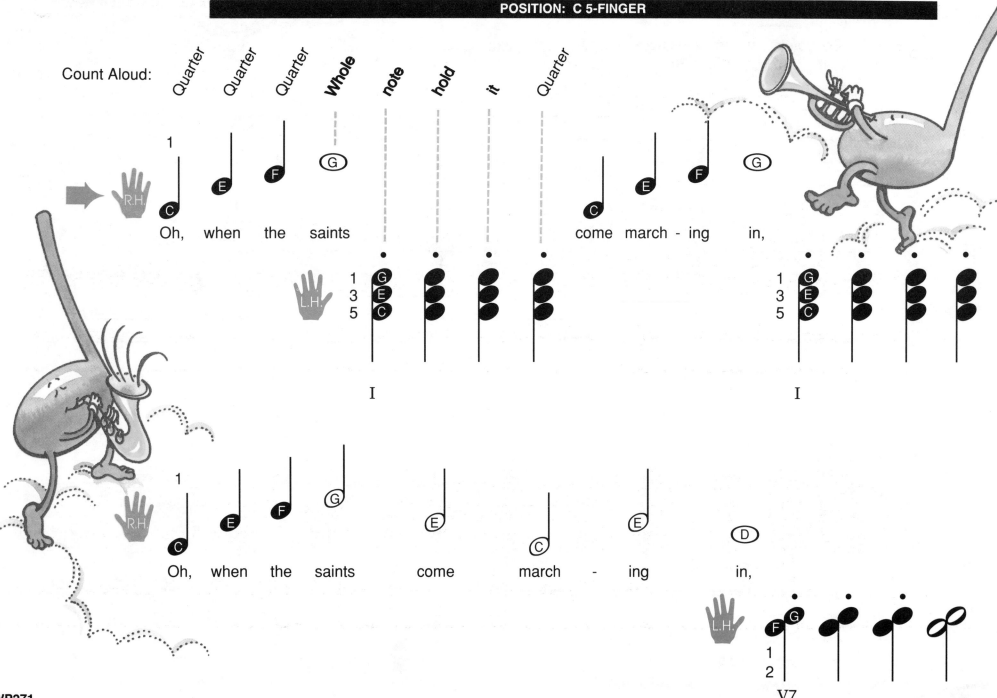

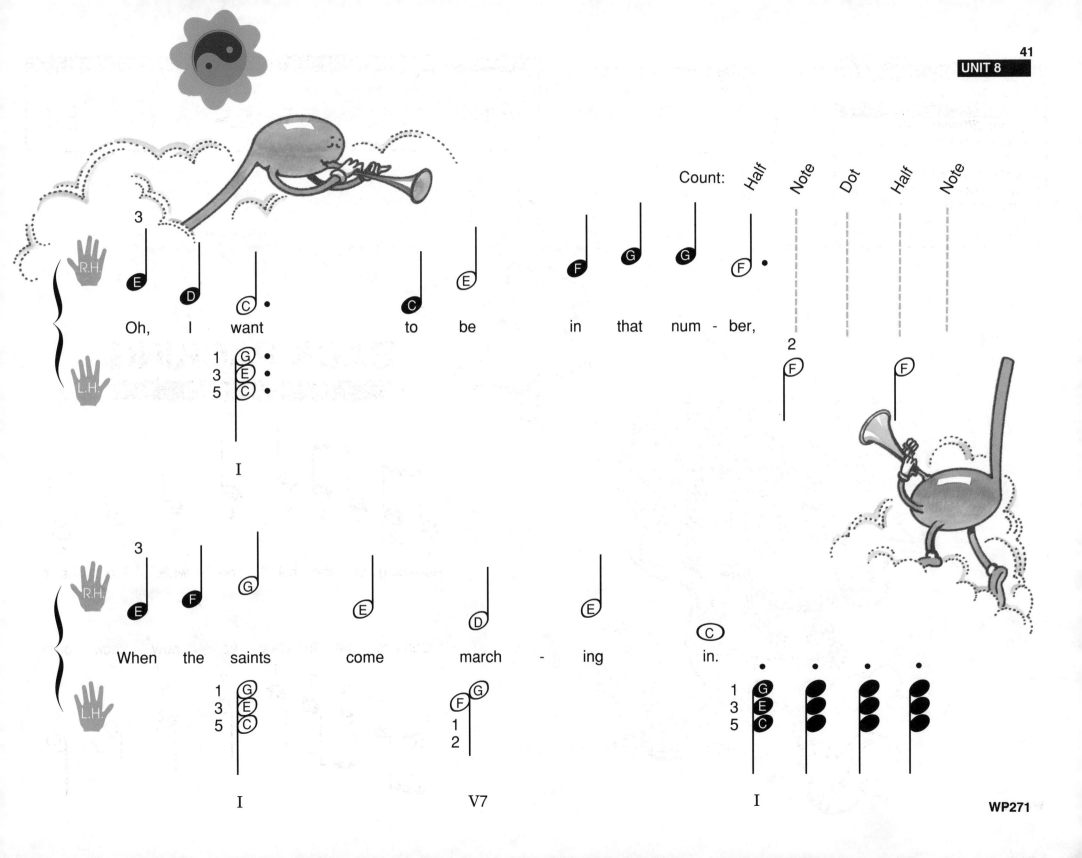

KEY AND CHORD REVIEW

1. Write the five-finger positions for the keys below.

C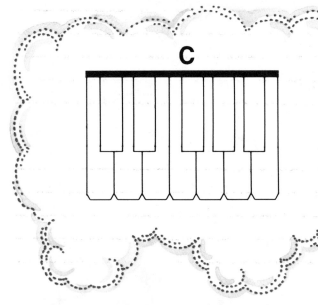

F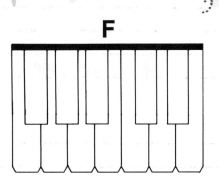

G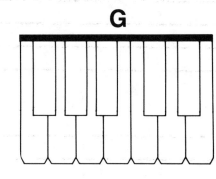

2. Write the I chords for the following keys.

C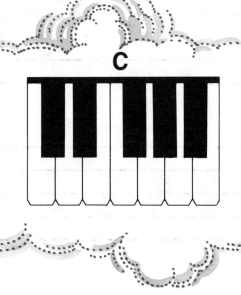

G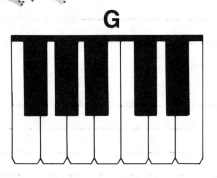

F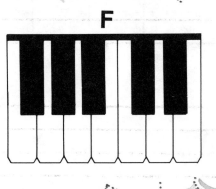

STAFF PAPER

TEACHER'S NOTES

We introduce concepts first in *Piano Party*. They are reinforced in *Theory and Ear Training Party* and *Performance Party*. Our goal is to give a minimum of three pieces from *Piano Party* and *Performance Party* to practice at home each week. *Theory and Ear Training Party* may be used at a slower pace; much of the work may be completed during the weekly lesson. Units are used to organize segments of material and are correlated in the three books. Some students may complete a whole unit each week while others may need more time.

UNIT 1 (pages 2-7)

2 OUR SCHOOL DRUMMER

8va is introduced.

5 TAPPING AND CLAPPING RHYTHMS

A fun way to portray or feel rhythm is to have students tap and clap.
X = clap hands together; – = tap hands on the closed fallboard.

6-7 KEY OF C STEPPING SONG

The C five-finger position is introduced. Steps are introduced.

Students will learn to read by steps when note reading is introduced.

UNIT 2 (pages 8-11)

8 BACK PACKING

10 GOIN' FISHIN'

UNIT 4 (pages 16-20)

16 KEY OF G SONG

The G five-finger position is introduced.

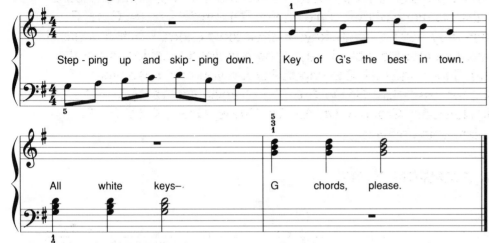

Step-ping up and skip-ping down. Key of G's the best in town.

All white keys— G chords, please.

17 THE BUSY AIRPORT

Lots of nois-y jets. Peo-ple rush-ing by.

Soon they'll all be on the planes and in the sky.

18 SATURDAY MORNINGS

Transposition is introduced.

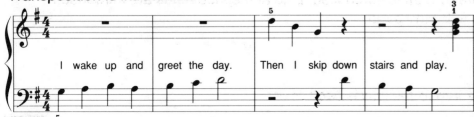

I wake up and greet the day. Then I skip down stairs and play.

19 WANDERING G CHORDS

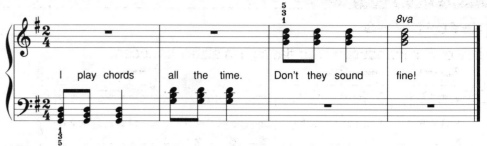

I play chords all the time. Don't they sound fine!

20 TAPPING AND CLAPPING NEW RHYTHMS

♫♫, ♩.,and ♪ are introduced. Counting note values enables a young student to play these rhythms.

UNIT 5 (pages 21-25)

22 THANKSGIVING DAY

1. Thanks-giv-ing Day and I can't wait. Din-ner's at two. Don't be late!
2. I will see Gram. She'll bring a treat. It's so much fun when we meet.

23 ALPHABET SKIPS UP AND DOWN

Alphabet skips prepare the student to name the lines and spaces on the staff.

24 BIKE RACE

See all the bi-cy-cles read-y to race. Who do you think will win first place?

25 HIDING AND SEEKING SKIPS

Playing skips and steps in various positions without looking at the keyboard enables the student to visualize the keyboard.

UNIT 6   (pages 26-31)

26 KEY OF F SONG

The key of F is introduced. The flat sign is also introduced.

27 HOLIDAY LIGHTS

28 YEAR AROUND CHORDS

31 WATCH THE CALENDAR

UNIT 7   (pages 32-36)

32 GROUP 1 KEYS

The twelve keys on the keyboard are divided into four groups according to the positions of their tonic chords. Group 1 keys are C, G, F because they have all white keys in their tonic chord. F is the unusual key because there is a black key in the five-finger position under the R.H. 4th finger and L.H. 2nd finger. For fun you could use types of cookies for examples: *Group 1 C G F:* Vanilla wafers; *Group 2 D A E:* Fig Newtons; *Group 3 Db Ab Eb:* Oreos; *Group 4 Gb Bb B:* Chocolate chip cookies.

33 THE MAGICAL HARP

34 THE GRAND STAFF

The Grand Staff is introduced. Line and space notes are introduced on the following page.

Please turn to the inside back cover.

PIANO PARTY

Certificate of Achievement

My name is _____. I am _____ years old.

I am learning to play the piano! I have completed **PIANO PARTY, Book B.**

My favorite three pieces in this book are:

_____

_____

_____

I have played pieces in the 5-finger positions of C, G, and F.
I have learned to draw the following notes: